2021-2022

Troop Leader Planner

Troop No :

Table Of Contents

Leader

Name : Drema Sparks	Cell No : (440) 506 2572	Background Checked : Y / N
Address : 4523 Oakhill Blvd. Lorain, OH 44053		
Email Address :		
Notes :		

Co Leaders and Volunteers

Name :	Cell No :	Background Checked : Y / N
Address :		
Email Address :		
Notes :		

Name :	Cell No :	Background Checked : Y / N
Address :		
Email Address :		
Notes :		

Name :	Cell No :	Background Checked : Y / N
Address :		
Email Address :		
Notes :		

Name :	Cell No :	Background Checked : Y / N
Address :		
Email Address :		
Notes :		

Name :	Cell No :	Background Checked : Y / N
Address :		
Email Address :		
Notes :		

Co Leaders and Volunteers

Name :	Cell No :	Background Checked : Y / N
Address :		
Email Address :		
Notes :		

Name :	Cell No :	Background Checked : Y / N
Address :		
Email Address :		
Notes :		

Name :	Cell No :	Background Checked : Y / N
Address :		
Email Address :		
Notes :		

Name :	Cell No :	Background Checked : Y / N
Address :		
Email Address :		
Notes :		

Name :	Cell No :	Background Checked : Y / N
Address :		
Email Address :		
Notes :		

Co Leaders and Volunteers

Name :	Cell No :	Background Checked : Y / N
Address :		
Email Address :		
Notes :		

Name :	Cell No :	Background Checked : Y / N
Address :		
Email Address :		
Notes :		

Name :	Cell No :	Background Checked : Y / N
Address :		
Email Address :		
Notes :		

Name :	Cell No :	Background Checked : Y / N
Address :		
Email Address :		
Notes :		

Name :	Cell No :	Background Checked : Y / N
Address :		
Email Address :		
Notes :		

TROOP ROSTER

Girl's Name :	Cell No :	School :
Parent's Name :	Cell No :	
Parent's Name :	Cell No :	
Address :	Email Address :	
Emergency Contact :	Cell No :	
Allergies :	Age :	Birthday :

Girl's Name :	Cell No :	School :
Parent's Name :	Cell No :	
Parent's Name :	Cell No :	
Address :	Email Address :	
Emergency Contact :	Cell No :	
Allergies :	Age :	Birthday :

Girl's Name :	Cell No :	School :
Parent's Name :	Cell No :	
Parent's Name :	Cell No :	
Address :	Email Address :	
Emergency Contact :	Cell No :	
Allergies :	Age :	Birthday :

Girl's Name :	Cell No :	School :
Parent's Name :	Cell No :	
Parent's Name :	Cell No :	
Address :	Email Address :	
Emergency Contact :	Cell No :	
Allergies :	Age :	Birthday :

TROOP ROSTER

Girl's Name :	Cell No :	School :
Parent's Name :	Cell No :	
Parent's Name :	Cell No :	
Address :	Email Address :	
Emergency Contact :	Cell No :	
Allergies :	Age :	Birthday :

Girl's Name :	Cell No :	School :
Parent's Name :	Cell No :	
Parent's Name :	Cell No :	
Address :	Email Address :	
Emergency Contact :	Cell No :	
Allergies :	Age :	Birthday :

Girl's Name :	Cell No :	School :
Parent's Name :	Cell No :	
Parent's Name :	Cell No :	
Address :	Email Address :	
Emergency Contact :	Cell No :	
Allergies :	Age :	Birthday :

Girl's Name :	Cell No :	School :
Parent's Name :	Cell No :	
Parent's Name :	Cell No :	
Address :	Email Address :	
Emergency Contact :	Cell No :	
Allergies :	Age :	Birthday :

TROOP ROSTER

Girl's Name :	Cell No :	School :
Parent's Name :	Cell No :	
Parent's Name :	Cell No :	
Address :	Email Address :	
Emergency Contact :	Cell No :	
Allergies :	Age :	Birthday :

Girl's Name :	Cell No :	School :
Parent's Name :	Cell No :	
Parent's Name :	Cell No :	
Address :	Email Address :	
Emergency Contact :	Cell No :	
Allergies :	Age :	Birthday :

Girl's Name :	Cell No :	School :
Parent's Name :	Cell No :	
Parent's Name :	Cell No :	
Address :	Email Address :	
Emergency Contact :	Cell No :	
Allergies :	Age :	Birthday :

Girl's Name :	Cell No :	School :
Parent's Name :	Cell No :	
Parent's Name :	Cell No :	
Address :	Email Address :	
Emergency Contact :	Cell No :	
Allergies :	Age :	Birthday :

TROOP ROSTER

Girl's Name :	Cell No :	School :
Parent's Name :	Cell No :	
Parent's Name :	Cell No :	
Address :	Email Address :	
Emergency Contact :	Cell No :	
Allergies :	Age :	Birthday :

Girl's Name :	Cell No :	School :
Parent's Name :	Cell No :	
Parent's Name :	Cell No :	
Address :	Email Address :	
Emergency Contact :	Cell No :	
Allergies :	Age :	Birthday :

Girl's Name :	Cell No :	School :
Parent's Name :	Cell No :	
Parent's Name :	Cell No :	
Address :	Email Address :	
Emergency Contact :	Cell No :	
Allergies :	Age :	Birthday :

Girl's Name :	Cell No :	School :
Parent's Name :	Cell No :	
Parent's Name :	Cell No :	
Address :	Email Address :	
Emergency Contact :	Cell No :	
Allergies :	Age :	Birthday :

Health Info

Girl's Name	Health Issues	Notes

Health Info

Girl's Name	Health Issues	Notes

Birthday Tracker

January	February	March

April	May	June

July	August	September

October	November	December

2021

January

S	M	T	W	T	F	S
					1	2
3	4	5	6	7	8	9
10	11	12	13	14	15	16
17	18	19	20	21	22	23
24	25	26	27	28	29	30
31						

February

S	M	T	W	T	F	S
	1	2	3	4	5	6
7	8	9	10	11	12	13
14	15	16	17	18	19	20
21	22	23	24	25	26	27
28						

March

S	M	T	W	T	F	S
	1	2	3	4	5	6
7	8	9	10	11	12	13
14	15	16	17	18	19	20
21	22	23	24	25	26	27
28	29	30	31			

April

S	M	T	W	T	F	S
				1	2	3
4	5	6	7	8	9	10
11	12	13	14	15	16	17
18	19	20	21	22	23	24
25	26	27	28	29	30	

May

S	M	T	W	T	F	S
						1
2	3	4	5	6	7	8
9	10	11	12	13	14	15
16	17	18	19	20	21	22
23	24	25	26	27	28	29
30	31					

June

S	M	T	W	T	F	S
		1	2	3	4	5
6	7	8	9	10	11	12
13	14	15	16	17	18	19
20	21	22	23	24	25	26
27	28	29	30			

July

S	M	T	W	T	F	S
				1	2	3
4	5	6	7	8	9	10
11	12	13	14	15	16	17
18	19	20	21	22	23	24
25	26	27	28	29	30	31

August

S	M	T	W	T	F	S
1	2	3	4	5	6	7
8	9	10	11	12	13	14
15	16	17	18	19	20	21
22	23	24	25	26	27	28
29	30	31				

September

S	M	T	W	T	F	S
			1	2	3	4
5	6	7	8	9	10	11
12	13	14	15	16	17	18
19	20	21	22	23	24	25
26	27	28	29	30		

October

S	M	T	W	T	F	S
					1	2
3	4	5	6	7	8	9
10	11	12	13	14	15	16
17	18	19	20	21	22	23
24	25	26	27	28	29	30
31						

November

S	M	T	W	T	F	S
	1	2	3	4	5	6
7	8	9	10	11	12	13
14	15	16	17	18	19	20
21	22	23	24	25	26	27
28	29	30				

December

S	M	T	W	T	F	S
			1	2	3	4
5	6	7	8	9	10	11
12	13	14	15	16	17	18
19	20	21	22	23	24	25
26	27	28	29	30	31	

2022

January
S	M	T	W	T	F	S
						1
2	3	4	5	6	7	8
9	10	11	12	13	14	15
16	17	18	19	20	21	22
23	24	25	26	27	28	29
30	31					

February
S	M	T	W	T	F	S
		1	2	3	4	5
6	7	8	9	10	11	12
13	14	15	16	17	18	19
20	21	22	23	24	25	26
27	28					

March
S	M	T	W	T	F	S
		1	2	3	4	5
6	7	8	9	10	11	12
13	14	15	16	17	18	19
20	21	22	23	24	25	26
27	28	29	30	31		

April
S	M	T	W	T	F	S
					1	2
3	4	5	6	7	8	9
10	11	12	13	14	15	16
17	18	19	20	21	22	23
24	25	26	27	28	29	30

May
S	M	T	W	T	F	S
1	2	3	4	5	6	7
8	9	10	11	12	13	14
15	16	17	18	19	20	21
22	23	24	25	26	27	28
29	30	31				

June
S	M	T	W	T	F	S
			1	2	3	4
5	6	7	8	9	10	11
12	13	14	15	16	17	18
19	20	21	22	23	24	25
26	27	28	29	30		

July
S	M	T	W	T	F	S
					1	2
3	4	5	6	7	8	9
10	11	12	13	14	15	16
17	18	19	20	21	22	23
24	25	26	27	28	29	30
31						

August
S	M	T	W	T	F	S
	1	2	3	4	5	6
7	8	9	10	11	12	13
14	15	16	17	18	19	20
21	22	23	24	25	26	27
28	29	30	31			

September
S	M	T	W	T	F	S
				1	2	3
4	5	6	7	8	9	10
11	12	13	14	15	16	17
18	19	20	21	22	23	24
25	26	27	28	29	30	

October
S	M	T	W	T	F	S
						1
2	3	4	5	6	7	8
9	10	11	12	13	14	15
16	17	18	19	20	21	22
23	24	25	26	27	28	29
30	31					

November
S	M	T	W	T	F	S
		1	2	3	4	5
6	7	8	9	10	11	12
13	14	15	16	17	18	19
20	21	22	23	24	25	26
27	28	29	30			

December
S	M	T	W	T	F	S
				1	2	3
4	5	6	7	8	9	10
11	12	13	14	15	16	17
18	19	20	21	22	23	24
25	26	27	28	29	30	31

July 2021

Sunday	Monday	Tuesday	Wednesday	Thursday	Friday	Saturday
				1	2	3
4	5	6	7	8	9	10
11	12	13	14	15	16	17
18	19	20	21	22	23	24
25	26	27	28	29	30	31

August 2021

Sunday	Monday	Tuesday	Wednesday	Thursday	Friday	Saturday
1	2	3	4	5	6	7
8	9	10	11	12	13	14
15	16	17	18	19	20	21
22	23	24	25	26	27	28
29	30	31				

September 2021

Sunday	Monday	Tuesday	Wednesday	Thursday	Friday	Saturday
			1	2	3	4
5	6	7	8	9	10	11
12	13	14	15	16	17	18
19	20	21	22	23	24	25
26	27	28	29	30		

_____

_____

_____

_____

October 2021

Sunday	Monday	Tuesday	Wednesday	Thursday	Friday	Saturday
					1	2
3	4	5	6	7	8	9
10	11	12	13	14	15	16
17	18	19	20	21	22	23
24	25	26	27	28	29	30
31						

_____
_____
_____
_____

November 2021

Sunday	Monday	Tuesday	Wednesday	Thursday	Friday	Saturday
	1	2	3	4	5	6
7	8	9	10	11	12	13
14	15	16	17	18	19	20
21	22	23	24	25	26	27
28	29	30				

December 2021

Sunday	Monday	Tuesday	Wednesday	Thursday	Friday	Saturday
			1	2	3	4
5	6	7	8	9	10	11
12	13	14	15	16	17	18
19	20	21	22	23	24	25
26	27	28	29	30	31	

January 2022

Sunday	Monday	Tuesday	Wednesday	Thursday	Friday	Saturday
						1
2	3	4	5	6	7	8
9	10	11	12	13	14	15
16	17	18	19	20	21	22
23	24	25	26	27	28	29
30	31					

_____

_____

_____

_____

February 2022

Sunday	Monday	Tuesday	Wednesday	Thursday	Friday	Saturday
		1	2	3	4	5
6	7	8	9	10	11	12
13	14	15	16	17	18	19
20	21	22	23	24	25	26
27	28					

March 2022

Sunday	Monday	Tuesday	Wednesday	Thursday	Friday	Saturday
		1	2	3	4	5
6	7	8	9	10	11	12
13	14	15	16	17	18	19
20	21	22	23	24	25	26
27	28	29	30	31		

_____

_____

_____

_____

April 2022

Sunday	Monday	Tuesday	Wednesday	Thursday	Friday	Saturday
					1	2
3	4	5	6	7	8	9
10	11	12	13	14	15	16
17	18	19	20	21	22	23
24	25	26	27	28	29	30

_____

_____

_____

_____

May 2022

Sunday	Monday	Tuesday	Wednesday	Thursday	Friday	Saturday
1	2	3	4	5	6	7
8	9	10	11	12	13	14
15	16	17	18	19	20	21
22	23	24	25	26	27	28
29	30	31				

June 2022

Sunday	Monday	Tuesday	Wednesday	Thursday	Friday	Saturday
			1	2	3	4
5	6	7	8	9	10	11
12	13	14	15	16	17	18
19	20	21	22	23	24	25
26	27	28	29	30		

_____
_____
_____
_____

July 2022

Sunday	Monday	Tuesday	Wednesday	Thursday	Friday	Saturday
					1	2
3	4	5	6	7	8	9
10	11	12	13	14	15	16
17	18	19	20	21	22	23
24	25	26	27	28	29	30
31						

August 2022

Sunday	Monday	Tuesday	Wednesday	Thursday	Friday	Saturday
	1	2	3	4	5	6
7	8	9	10	11	12	13
14	15	16	17	18	19	20
21	22	23	24	25	26	27
28	29	30	31			

Attendance Tracker

Date	Meeting / Event	Girls' Names																

Attendance Tracker

Date	Meeting / Event	Girls' Names																		

Attendance Tracker

Date	Meeting / Event	Girls' Names																	

Snack Signup Sheet

Meeting Date	Girl's Name	Notes

Snack Signup Sheet

Meeting Date	Girl's Name	Notes

Meeting / Event Planner

Date and Place of Meeting / Event :

Pre-Meeting Preparation :

Opening Ceremony :

Activities :

Supplies If Any Needed :

Cleanup and Closing :

Notes :

Meeting / Event Planner

Date and Place of Meeting / Event :

Pre-Meeting Preparation :

Opening Ceremony :

Activities :

Supplies If Any Needed :

Cleanup and Closing :

Notes :

Meeting / Event Planner

Date and Place of Meeting / Event :

Pre-Meeting Preparation :

Opening Ceremony :

Activities :

Supplies If Any Needed :

Cleanup and Closing :

Notes :

Meeting / Event Planner

Date and Place of Meeting / Event :

Pre-Meeting Preparation :

Opening Ceremony :

Activities :

Supplies If Any Needed :

Cleanup and Closing :

Notes :

Meeting / Event Planner

Date and Place of Meeting / Event :

Pre-Meeting Preparation :

Opening Ceremony :

Activities :

Supplies If Any Needed :

Cleanup and Closing :

Notes :

Meeting / Event Planner

Date and Place of Meeting / Event :

Pre-Meeting Preparation :

Opening Ceremony :

Activities :

Supplies If Any Needed :

Cleanup and Closing :

Notes :

Meeting / Event Planner

Date and Place of Meeting / Event :

Pre-Meeting Preparation :

Opening Ceremony :

Activities :

Supplies If Any Needed :

Cleanup and Closing :

Notes :

Meeting / Event Planner

Date and Place of Meeting / Event :

Pre-Meeting Preparation :

Opening Ceremony :

Activities :

Supplies If Any Needed :

Cleanup and Closing :

Notes :

Meeting / Event Planner

Date and Place of Meeting / Event :

Pre-Meeting Preparation :

Opening Ceremony :

Activities :

Supplies If Any Needed :

Cleanup and Closing :

Notes :

Meeting / Event Planner

Date and Place of Meeting / Event :

Pre-Meeting Preparation :

Opening Ceremony :

Activities :

Supplies If Any Needed :

Cleanup and Closing :

Notes :

Meeting / Event Planner

Date and Place of Meeting / Event :

Pre-Meeting Preparation :

Opening Ceremony :

Activities :

Supplies If Any Needed :

Cleanup and Closing :

Notes :

Meeting / Event Planner

Date and Place of Meeting / Event :

Pre-Meeting Preparation :

Opening Ceremony :

Activities :

Supplies If Any Needed :

Cleanup and Closing :

Notes :

Meeting / Event Planner

Date and Place of Meeting / Event :

Pre-Meeting Preparation :

Opening Ceremony :

Activities :

Supplies If Any Needed :

Cleanup and Closing :

Notes :

Meeting / Event Planner

Date and Place of Meeting / Event :

Pre-Meeting Preparation :

Opening Ceremony :

Activities :

Supplies If Any Needed :

Cleanup and Closing :

Notes :

Meeting / Event Planner

Date and Place of Meeting / Event :

Pre-Meeting Preparation :

Opening Ceremony :

Activities :

Supplies If Any Needed :

Cleanup and Closing :

Notes :

Meeting / Event Planner

Date and Place of Meeting / Event :

Pre-Meeting Preparation :

Opening Ceremony :

Activities :

Supplies If Any Needed :

Cleanup and Closing :

Notes :

Meeting / Event Planner

Date and Place of Meeting / Event :

Pre-Meeting Preparation :

Opening Ceremony :

Activities :

Supplies If Any Needed :

Cleanup and Closing :

Notes :

Meeting / Event Planner

Date and Place of Meeting / Event :

Pre-Meeting Preparation :

Opening Ceremony :

Activities :

Supplies If Any Needed :

Cleanup and Closing :

Notes :

Meeting / Event Planner

Date and Place of Meeting / Event :

Pre-Meeting Preparation :

Opening Ceremony :

Activities :

Supplies If Any Needed :

Cleanup and Closing :

Notes :

Meeting / Event Planner

Date and Place of Meeting / Event :

Pre-Meeting Preparation :

Opening Ceremony :

Activities :

Supplies If Any Needed :

Cleanup and Closing :

Notes :

Meeting / Event Planner

Date and Place of Meeting / Event :

Pre-Meeting Preparation :

Opening Ceremony :

Activities :

Supplies If Any Needed :

Cleanup and Closing :

Notes :

Meeting / Event Planner

Date and Place of Meeting / Event :

Pre-Meeting Preparation :

Opening Ceremony :

Activities :

Supplies If Any Needed :

Cleanup and Closing :

Notes :

Meeting / Event Planner

Date and Place of Meeting / Event :

Pre-Meeting Preparation :

Opening Ceremony :

Activities :

Supplies If Any Needed :

Cleanup and Closing :

Notes :

Meeting / Event Planner

Date and Place of Meeting / Event :

Pre-Meeting Preparation :

Opening Ceremony :

Activities :

Supplies If Any Needed :

Cleanup and Closing :

Notes :

Meeting / Event Planner

Date and Place of Meeting / Event :

Pre-Meeting Preparation :

Opening Ceremony :

Activities :

Supplies If Any Needed :

Cleanup and Closing :

Notes :

Meeting / Event Planner

Date and Place of Meeting / Event :

Pre-Meeting Preparation :

Opening Ceremony :

Activities :

Supplies If Any Needed :

Cleanup and Closing :

Notes :

Meeting / Event Planner

Date and Place of Meeting / Event :

Pre-Meeting Preparation :

Opening Ceremony :

Activities :

Supplies If Any Needed :

Cleanup and Closing :

Notes :

Meeting / Event Planner

Date and Place of Meeting / Event :

Pre-Meeting Preparation :

Opening Ceremony :

Activities :

Supplies If Any Needed :

Cleanup and Closing :

Notes :

Meeting / Event Planner

Date and Place of Meeting / Event :

Pre-Meeting Preparation :

Opening Ceremony :

Activities :

Supplies If Any Needed :

Cleanup and Closing :

Notes :

Meeting / Event Planner

Date and Place of Meeting / Event :

Pre-Meeting Preparation :

Opening Ceremony :

Activities :

Supplies If Any Needed :

Cleanup and Closing :

Notes :

Meeting / Event Planner

Date and Place of Meeting / Event :

Pre-Meeting Preparation :

Opening Ceremony :

Activities :

Supplies If Any Needed :

Cleanup and Closing :

Notes :

Meeting / Event Planner

Date and Place of Meeting / Event :

Pre-Meeting Preparation :

Opening Ceremony :

Activities :

Supplies If Any Needed :

Cleanup and Closing :

Notes :

Meeting / Event Planner

Date and Place of Meeting / Event :

Pre-Meeting Preparation :

Opening Ceremony :

Activities :

Supplies If Any Needed :

Cleanup and Closing :

Notes :

Meeting / Event Planner

Date and Place of Meeting / Event :

Pre-Meeting Preparation :

Opening Ceremony :

Activities :

Supplies If Any Needed :

Cleanup and Closing :

Notes :

Meeting / Event Planner

Date and Place of Meeting / Event :

Pre-Meeting Preparation :

Opening Ceremony :

Activities :

Supplies If Any Needed :

Cleanup and Closing :

Notes :

Meeting / Event Planner

Date and Place of Meeting / Event :

Pre-Meeting Preparation :

Opening Ceremony :

Activities :

Supplies If Any Needed :

Cleanup and Closing :

Notes :

Meeting / Event Planner

Date and Place of Meeting / Event :

Pre-Meeting Preparation :

Opening Ceremony :

Activities :

Supplies If Any Needed :

Cleanup and Closing :

Notes :

Meeting / Event Planner

Date and Place of Meeting / Event :

Pre-Meeting Preparation :

Opening Ceremony :

Activities :

Supplies If Any Needed :

Cleanup and Closing :

Notes :

Meeting / Event Planner

Date and Place of Meeting / Event :

Pre-Meeting Preparation :

Opening Ceremony :

Activities :

Supplies If Any Needed :

Cleanup and Closing :

Notes :

Meeting / Event Planner

Date and Place of Meeting / Event :

Pre-Meeting Preparation :

Opening Ceremony :

Activities :

Supplies If Any Needed :

Cleanup and Closing :

Notes :

Badge and Patch Tracker

Date	Badges and Patch Description	Girls' Names													

Badge and Patch Tracker

Date	Badges and Patch Description	Girls' Names																	

Forms and Paperwork Tracker

Date	Forms or Paperwork To Be Done	Girls' Names															

Forms and Paperwork Tracker

Date	Forms or Paperwork To Be Done	Girls' Names																	

Volunteer Signup Sheet

Event Date	Description of Event	Volunteers

Volunteer Signup Sheet

Event Date	Description of Event	Volunteers

Volunteer Signup Sheet

Event Date	Description of Event	Volunteers

Volunteer Signup Sheet

Event Date	Description of Event	Volunteers

Troop Dues and Fees Tracker

Date	Description (Membership Dues, Uniform, FieldTrip Fees etc.,)	Girls' Names (Mark When Paid)																

Troop Dues and Fees Tracker

Date	Description (Membership Dues, Uniform, FieldTrip Fees etc.,)	Girls' Names (Mark When Paid)																		

Troop Dues and Fees Tracker

Date	Description (Membership Dues, Uniform, FieldTrip Fees etc.,)	Girls' Names (Mark When Paid)																		

Troop Dues and Fees Tracker

Date	Description (Membership Dues, Uniform, FieldTrip Fees etc.,)	Girls' Names (Mark When Paid)																		

Financial Ledger

Date	Description	Income $	Expense $	Balance $

Financial Ledger

Date	Description	Income $	Expense $	Balance $

Financial Ledger

Date	Description	Income $	Expense $	Balance $

Financial Ledger

Date	Description	Income $	Expense $	Balance $

Checking Account Tracker

Bank Name :	Address :
Phone Number :	Hours of Operation :
Account Number :	Routing Number :

Date	Transaction	Withdrawal	Deposit	Balance

Checking Account Tracker

Date	Transaction	Withdrawal	Deposit	Balance

Checking Account Tracker

Date	Transaction	Withdrawal	Deposit	Balance

Checking Account Tracker

Date	Transaction	Withdrawal	Deposit	Balance

Individual Girls' Product Sales Tracker

Date	Product	Girls' Names																

Individual Girls' Product Sales Tracker

Date	Product	Girls' Names																	

Individual Girls' Product Sales Tracker

Date	Product	Girls' Names																			

Individual Girls' Product Sales Tracker

Date	Product	Girls' Names																	

Individual Girls' Product Sales Tracker

Date	Product	Girls' Names																			

Individual Girls' Product Sales Tracker

Date	Product	Girls' Names																	

Booth Sales Tracker

Booth Location :   Date :

Product Name							
Price Per Box							
No of Boxes at the Start							
No of Boxes at the End							
Total No of Boxes Sold							
Total $ Earned							

Girl's Name	Starting Time	End Time	No of hours	No of Boxes Sold

Total No of Boxes Sold :	**Starting Cash Amount :**
	Ending Cash Amount :
$$ in Donations :	**Credit Card Sales :**

Total Booth Sales Profit :

Booth Sales Tracker

Booth Location :   **Date :**

Product Name								
Price Per Box								
No of Boxes at the Start								
No of Boxes at the End								
Total No of Boxes Sold								
Total $ Earned								

Girl's Name	Starting Time	End Time	No of hours	No of Boxes Sold

Total No of Boxes Sold :	**Starting Cash Amount :**
	Ending Cash Amount :
$$ in Donations :	**Credit Card Sales :**

Total Booth Sales Profit :

Booth Sales Tracker

Booth Location :   Date :

Product Name							
Price Per Box							
No of Boxes at the Start							
No of Boxes at the End							
Total No of Boxes Sold							
Total $ Earned							

Girl's Name	Starting Time	End Time	No of hours	No of Boxes Sold

Total No of Boxes Sold :	**Starting Cash Amount :**
	Ending Cash Amount :
$$ in Donations :	**Credit Card Sales :**

Total Booth Sales Profit :

Booth Sales Tracker

Booth Location :   **Date :**

Product Name							
Price Per Box							
No of Boxes at the Start							
No of Boxes at the End							
Total No of Boxes Sold							
Total $ Earned							

Girl's Name	Starting Time	End Time	No of hours	No of Boxes Sold

Total No of Boxes Sold :	**Starting Cash Amount :**	
	Ending Cash Amount :	
$$ in Donations :	**Credit Card Sales :**	

Total Booth Sales Profit :

Booth Sales Tracker

Booth Location :   **Date :**

Product Name							
Price Per Box							
No of Boxes at the Start							
No of Boxes at the End							
Total No of Boxes Sold							
Total $ Earned							

Girl's Name	Starting Time	End Time	No of hours	No of Boxes Sold

Total No of Boxes Sold :	**Starting Cash Amount :**
	Ending Cash Amount :
$$ in Donations :	**Credit Card Sales :**

Total Booth Sales Profit :

Booth Sales Tracker

Booth Location :   **Date :**

Product Name								
Price Per Box								
No of Boxes at the Start								
No of Boxes at the End								
Total No of Boxes Sold								
Total $ Earned								

Girl's Name	Starting Time	End Time	No of hours	No of Boxes Sold

Total No of Boxes Sold :	Starting Cash Amount :
	Ending Cash Amount :
$$ in Donations :	Credit Card Sales :

Total Booth Sales Profit :

Booth Sales Tracker

Booth Location :   Date :

Product Name							
Price Per Box							
No of Boxes at the Start							
No of Boxes at the End							
Total No of Boxes Sold							
Total $ Earned							

Girl's Name	Starting Time	End Time	No of hours	No of Boxes Sold

Total No of Boxes Sold :	**Starting Cash Amount :**
	Ending Cash Amount :
$$ in Donations :	**Credit Card Sales :**

Total Booth Sales Profit :

Booth Sales Tracker

Booth Location :   **Date :**

Product Name								
Price Per Box								
No of Boxes at the Start								
No of Boxes at the End								
Total No of Boxes Sold								

Total $ Earned								

Girl's Name	Starting Time	End Time	No of hours	No of Boxes Sold

Total No of Boxes Sold :	**Starting Cash Amount :**
	Ending Cash Amount :
$$ in Donations :	**Credit Card Sales :**

Total Booth Sales Profit :

Booth Sales Tracker

Booth Location :   **Date :**

Product Name								
Price Per Box								
No of Boxes at the Start								
No of Boxes at the End								
Total No of Boxes Sold								
Total $ Earned								

Girl's Name	Starting Time	End Time	No of hours	No of Boxes Sold

Total No of Boxes Sold :	**Starting Cash Amount :**
	Ending Cash Amount :
$$ in Donations :	**Credit Card Sales :**

Total Booth Sales Profit :

Booth Sales Tracker

Booth Location :   **Date :**

Product Name							
Price Per Box							
No of Boxes at the Start							
No of Boxes at the End							
Total No of Boxes Sold							
Total $ Earned							

Girl's Name	Starting Time	End Time	No of hours	No of Boxes Sold

Total No of Boxes Sold :	**Starting Cash Amount :**
	Ending Cash Amount :
$$ in Donations :	**Credit Card Sales :**

Total Booth Sales Profit :

Booth Sales Tracker

Booth Location :   Date :

Product Name								
Price Per Box								
No of Boxes at the Start								
No of Boxes at the End								
Total No of Boxes Sold								
Total $ Earned								

Girl's Name	Starting Time	End Time	No of hours	No of Boxes Sold

Total No of Boxes Sold :

$$ in Donations :

Starting Cash Amount :

Ending Cash Amount :

Credit Card Sales :

Total Booth Sales Profit :

Booth Sales Tracker

Booth Location :   **Date :**

Product Name							
Price Per Box							
No of Boxes at the Start							
No of Boxes at the End							
Total No of Boxes Sold							

Total $ Earned							

Girl's Name	Starting Time	End Time	No of hours	No of Boxes Sold

Total No of Boxes Sold :	**Starting Cash Amount :**
	Ending Cash Amount :
$$ in Donations :	**Credit Card Sales :**

Total Booth Sales Profit :

Notes and To-Do List

Notes	Date :

Notes and To-Do List

Notes	Date :

Notes and To-Do List

Notes	Date :

Notes and To-Do List

Notes	Date :

- [ ]
- [ ]
- [ ]
- [ ]
- [ ]
- [ ]
- [ ]
- [ ]
- [ ]
- [ ]
- [ ]

Notes and To-Do List

Notes	Date :

Notes and To-Do List

Notes	Date :

☐
☐
☐
☐
☐
☐
☐
☐
☐
☐
☐

Notes and To-Do List

Notes	Date :

Notes and To-Do List

Notes	Date :

- [ ]
- [ ]
- [ ]
- [ ]
- [ ]
- [ ]
- [ ]
- [ ]
- [ ]
- [ ]
- [ ]

Notes and To-Do List

Notes	Date :

Notes and To-Do List

Notes	Date :

Notes and To-Do List

Notes	Date :

☐
☐
☐
☐
☐
☐
☐
☐
☐
☐
☐

Notes and To-Do List

Notes	Date :

Notes and To-Do List

Notes	Date :

Notes and To-Do List

Notes	Date :

Notes and To-Do List

Notes	Date :

- [ ] _____
- [ ] _____
- [ ] _____
- [ ] _____
- [ ] _____
- [ ] _____
- [ ] _____
- [ ] _____
- [ ] _____
- [ ] _____
- [ ] _____

Notes and To-Do List

Notes	Date :

- [ ]
- [ ]
- [ ]
- [ ]
- [ ]
- [ ]
- [ ]
- [ ]
- [ ]
- [ ]
- [ ]

Notes and To-Do List

Notes	Date :

☐
☐
☐
☐
☐
☐
☐
☐
☐
☐
☐

Notes and To-Do List

Notes	Date :

Notes and To-Do List

Notes	Date :

Notes and To-Do List

Notes	Date :

- [ ]
- [ ]
- [ ]
- [ ]
- [ ]
- [ ]
- [ ]
- [ ]
- [ ]
- [ ]
- [ ]

Made in the USA
Monee, IL
06 November 2021